CULTURE IN ACTION

Playing the Spoons

AND OTHER CURIOUS INSTRUMENTS

Liz Miles

www.raintreepublishers.co.uk

Visit our website to find out more information about Raintree books.

To order:

☎ Phone 0845 6044371

📄 Fax +44 (0) 1865 312263

💻 Email myorders@raintreepublishers.co.uk

Customers from outside the UK please telephone +44 1865 312262

Raintree is an imprint of Capstone Global Library Limited, a company incorporated in England and Wales having its registered office at 7 Pilgrim Street, London, EC4V 6LB – Registered company number: 6695582

Edited by Louise Galpine and Diyan Leake
Designed by Victoria Allen
Original illustrations © Capstone Global Library Ltd 2011
Illustrated by Randy Schirz
Picture research by Hannah Taylor
Originated by Capstone Global Library Ltd
Printed in and bound in China by CTPS

ISBN 978 1 406 21696 7 (hardback)
14 13 12 11 10
10 9 8 7 6 5 4 3 2 1

British Library Cataloguing in Publication Data
Miles, Liz -- Playing the spoons and other curious instruments.
– (Culture in action)
784.1'9-dc22
A full catalogue record for this book is available from the British Library.

Acknowledgements
We would like to thank the following for permission to reproduce photographs: Alamy Images pp. **7** (© Peter Horree), **8** (© Interfoto), **12** (© The Art Gallery Collection), **18** (© PCL), **23** (© Eddie Gerald), **25** (© DigitalVues), **26** (© Suzy Bennett); Corbis pp. **14** top (Sandro Vannini), **14** bottom (Reuters/Jayanta Shaw), **19** (Jose Fuste Raga), **20** (Mark Bryan Makela); Courtesy of Linda Manzer p. **16** (Photo: Brian Pickell); Getty Images pp. **6** (Michael Ochs Archives/Larry Hulst), **9** (National Geographic), **13** (APIC), **22** (Dorling Kindersley/Rob Reichenfeld); Lebrecht Music & Arts pp. **4** (Chris Christodoulou), **10** (© Graham Salter); Photolibrary p. **17** (Lebrecht Music & Arts); Rex Features pp. **24** (Patrick Frilet), **29** (Donald Cooper).

Cover photograph © Capstone Publishers (Karon Dubke).

We would like to thank Patrick Allen and Jackie Murphy for their invaluable help in the preparation of this book.

Every effort has been made to contact copyright holders of material reproduced in this book. Any omissions will be rectified in subsequent printings if notice is given to the publisher.

Author

Liz Miles is an experienced author of non-fiction and fiction for children, with over 60 published titles.

Literacy consultant

Jackie Murphy is Director of Arts at a centre of teaching and learning. She works with teachers, artists, and school leaders internationally.

Expert

Patrick Allen is an award-winning author and music educator, whose work as an Advanced Skills Teacher of Music takes him into schools, colleges, and universities throughout the UK.

Contents

Some words are printed in bold, **like this**. You can find out
what they mean by looking in the glossary on page 30.

The world's strangest instruments

Have you ever heard a seashell horn, a serpent, or a rainstick? Hundreds of amazing instruments like these are played around the world. Some unusual instruments are traditional and have been played for hundreds of years. Others are modern-day record-breakers, such as the biggest guitar in the world, which is nearly as long as a bus. It was made by high school pupils and their teacher in Texas, USA.

What's different?

Instruments around the world can vary enormously. **Western** string quartets (groups of four musicians) often include a cello, two violins, and a viola. In India, string instruments are different. A small group of string players usually includes a sitar, vinas, and sarangis. Different cultures have developed different instruments.

This group is playing traditional Indian stringed instruments: sarangis (front row), a tanpura (back row, left), and a rabab (back row, right).

Naming instruments

World instruments are grouped by how they make sound. Instruments in the same group can look very different. String instruments, such as a violin or a sitar, are known as **chordophones**, but a violin is small, while a sitar has a long **neck**.

The table below shows how world instruments are grouped. You may already know the names of groups used in Western orchestras.

Serpent

Have you ever heard of a serpent? It is an **aerophone** instrument, shaped like a snake. Stretched out, a serpent would stand taller than an adult.

World instrument group	Western orchestral group	What makes the sound?	Examples of instruments
aerophones	wind and brass	**vibrating** mass(es) of air	recorders and bagpipes
chordophones	string	vibrating, stretched string(s)	violins and sitars
electrophones	electronic	electronics	electric organs and **synthesizers**
idiophones	**percussion**	material, such as wood or metal, that the instrument is made from	rattles and steel drums
membranophones	percussion	vibrating stretched skin or **membrane**	kettledrums and **kazoos**

Dance to the beat

Dancing to music with a strong beat is great fun. **Percussion** instruments (**idiophones** and **membranophones**) can get you moving fast or slow to the beat they produce. Some, such as xylophones, also play musical notes.

Many of the oldest idiophones, such as rattles and clappers, were used by people of early **civilizations**, such as the ancient Egyptians. Drums have been played for hundreds of years in ceremonies and for armies to march to.

All sorts of drums

Most drums are membranophones. A **membrane** or animal skin (leather) is stretched over a hollow vessel, such as a pot or vase. The sound comes from the **vibration** of the moving skin. There are all kinds of drums and many are named after their shape: barrel, goblet, footed, and long.

Not all drums are played by hitting them! African **friction** drums are rubbed with the fingers or a cloth. Some friction drums have a stick pushed through the skin. The player moves the stick to make the sound.

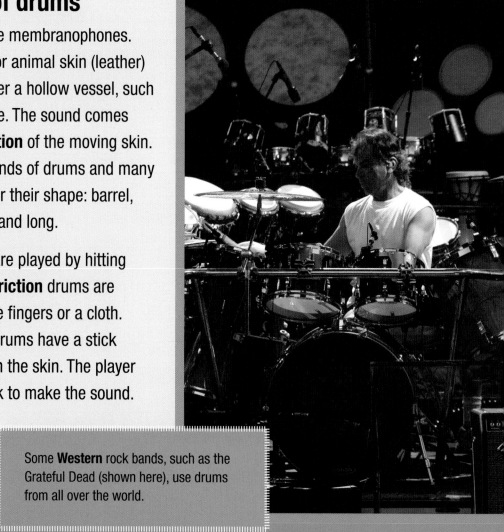

Some **Western** rock bands, such as the Grateful Dead (shown here), use drums from all over the world.

A gamelan orchestra includes gongs and drums.

Gamelan orchestra

Gamelan orchestras are traditional in Indonesia. The repeated rhythm and melody they create draws in listeners. Most of the instruments are hit with a beater or small hammer. Gamelan performances can last all night – but the people in the audience are allowed to come and go!

Cones and bones

Some of the oldest friction instruments were pairs of bones, shells, pine cones, or sticks. They were simply rubbed together.

Rites and rituals

Many idiophones (such as bells and gongs) are played in temples or as part of ceremonies. Some are made from metal. Others are made from natural materials such as wood, **gourds** (types of large fruit, such as squash or pumpkins), or teeth.

Clappers and scrapers

Clappers, such as castanets, make a "clack" as two pieces are knocked together. The ancient Egyptians made clappers from hippopotamus teeth and elephant tusks. Scrapers have a surface that makes a sound when it is scraped.

This African scraper was made from a gourd.

Rattles

Rattles, such as shakers and maracas, are hollow instruments filled with small, dry objects such as seeds or rice. Native American rattles are made from nuts, bones, or animal claws. A rattle from Arizona was made from a rat's skin. Native American shamans (healers) use rattles made from tortoise shells to call up spirits and heal people.

Legend of the mokugyo

The mokugyo is a fish-shaped Japanese instrument similar to the wooden block played by percussionists in Western orchestras. It is hit with a stick to make a sound. A legend tells of a fish that helped a monk cross a flooded river. The monk promised to do something for the fish in exchange, but forgot. When the monk came back, the angry fish let the monk nearly drown. Annoyed with the fish, the monk made a wooden copy of it and beat it with a wooden hammer.

Today, the mokugyo is played in temples in Japan.

Special effects

Some idiophones make sound effects. The sound of a cracking whip is popular in modern orchestras. It is made by slapping two small planks together.

Stormy sounds

The sounds of a storm can be created with these instruments:

• *Thunder sheets* are made from a hanging metal sheet. The player shakes or hits the sheet to make a crash.

• *Wind machines* are a barrel or drum with outer layers of wood and canvas (strong material). The player turns the barrel with a handle. As it turns, the wood and canvas rub. The rubbing makes a howling sound.

• *Rainsticks* are long, thin rattles. A hollow tube is made from a tree branch, bamboo cane, or cactus. As you tip the stick, small beads or stones inside fall from one end to the other. They sound like raindrops.

In the past, South American rainsticks were used in ceremonies, in the hope that they would bring rain.

Playing the spoons

Some of the simplest idiophones are clappers, in which one thing is hit against another, like castanets or spoons. Borrow two spoons, and find out how a simple instrument can be very effective (with practice!).

Steps to follow:

1. Hold the spoons.

- Place the spoons, back to back, on either side of your index finger (there should be a space between the backs of the spoons).

- Both spoons should be against the middle bone of your index finger.

- Wrap your fingers into your palm to grip the spoons.

- Fold the thumb down (see the picture).

2. Put your other hand, palm down, a few inches above your thigh. Knock the spoons back and forth between your palm and thigh.

3. Try this too: spread the fingers of your open palm, and drag the spoons across your fingers to make several fast sounds.

4. You could play your favourite track of music and accompany it on the spoons. Or try forks!

Simple strings

Chordophones range from hand-held banjos to pianos too big to get through a door. But they all have strings, which are plucked, struck, or **bowed** to make them **vibrate**. The vibrating strings make the sounds.

Musical bows

A musical bow looks like an archer's longbow. Some African peoples used the same bow for both hunting and playing music! It was made with one string and one curved piece of wood.

Some players use their mouth as a **resonator**, which creates more space to make the sound louder. Others attach the bow to a **gourd**, wooden bowl, or even a baked bean tin! All these act as a resonator, and when the air inside vibrates with the strings, it amplifies the sound (makes it louder).

The strings on ancient Greek lyres were made from a plant called hemp.

Hermes' lyre

In ancient Greek mythology it is said that Hermes (the messenger of the gods) invented the lyre. He stretched seven strings made from cow gut across a tortoise shell.

Ancient lyres

Lyres have four sides and a box at the bottom, which acts as the resonator. They have been played for thousands of years. Lyres from Sumer (an ancient **civilization**) have been found that are 4,500 years old. Lyres are still popular today in the African countries of Eritrea and Ethiopia.

Harps

Harps in the orchestra are upright. Other harps are horizontal, like a table. Many ancient harps were played in royal courts. Only the very rich could afford them. Even today, a new, gold-covered harp can cost thousands of pounds.

The koto is a Japanese harp-like instrument. The musician kneels on the ground to play it.

A hole in the ground

Some of the oldest zithers were just a string stretched over a hole in the ground! They were made in Africa and South East Asia. The string was beaten with sticks. Today, zithers have 30 to 45 strings stretched across a resonator.

Long-necked sitar

The sitar has a very long **neck**. At first, sitars were played mainly in India. But in the 1960s a famous sitar player, Ravi Shankar, toured the world. Soon **Westerners** were playing the sitar and buying sitar recordings, too. People loved the instrument's often high-pitched, buzzing sound.

In the Middle Ages, zither strings were plucked with a tool called a plectrum, made from the central rib of a crow's feather.

Anoushka Shankar

Anoushka was born in London in 1981. Her father taught her to play the sitar. She started touring at the age of 13 and got her first record deal three years later. Since then she has performed all around the world.

Can you play the pyramid?

Pianos are like zithers, but they have **keys** attached to hammers which strike the strings. All sorts of pianos were made in the 1700s, such as:

- Pyramid and giraffe pianos: the strings are strung on upright boards. The piano names describe the board shapes.

- Harp piano: like an upright harp, you can see all the strings.

- Orphica: a small piano, light enough to carry in one hand.

- Janko piano: this strange piano had six rows of keys instead of one. The inventor thought it would be easier for the musician's fingers to reach all the keys. But it never caught on – people did not want to have to learn a whole new way of playing the piano.

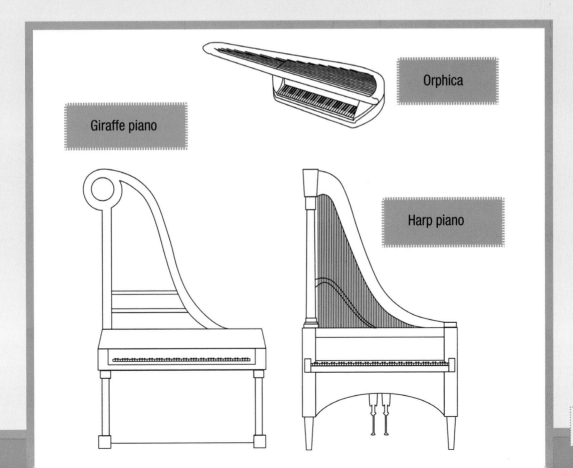

Orphica

Giraffe piano

Harp piano

Strange guitars

Question: When is a guitar not a guitar? Answer: When it is mixed with something else! A guitar-lute has six strings like a guitar, but a lute-shaped body. The guitar-banjo has six strings like a guitar, but a skin-covered body like a banjo.

All shapes and sizes

Most pop bands have electric guitars. Electricity amplifies the sound of electric guitars. When playing live on stage, some musicians have electric guitars that look as exciting as they sound. The main body of the guitar might be shaped like an arrow, a star, or even a snake!

Multi-necked guitars have more than one neck, each with a full set of strings. Some electric guitars have five or more necks. Only quick-movers can play them!

How many necks?

The Pikasso guitar has 4 necks and 42 strings. It creates a trance-like sound. Linda Manzer, a Canadian string-instrument maker, handmade it for an American jazz guitarist.

Linda Manzer designed and built the Pikasso because she was asked to make a guitar with as many strings as possible.

Electronic keyboards

Electronic instruments produce their sound electronically. Some of the first electronic keyboards (**electrophones**) look odd today. The ondes martenot was built in 1928 by a Frenchman called Maurice Martenot. It had three loudspeakers (one is lyre-shaped), which produced different types of sound. Today, all kinds of new sounds can be made with one electronic **synthesizer** and its keyboard.

A synthesizer can weave special effects like bird song and explosions into music. A synthesizer can also mimic all other instruments. Sometimes musicians may lose their jobs because one synthesizer can play the parts of different instruments.

The ondes martenot was one of the first electronic instruments.

Blow it!

Traditional **aerophones** vary widely around the world. Trumpets made from conch shells are played in the Marquesas Islands, in the South Pacific. Mouth organs made from bamboo pipes are found in South East Asia. They can be up to 3 metres (10 feet) long.

Didgeridoo

The didgeridoo is like a simple wooden trumpet. Aboriginal (native) people in Australia developed it and, traditionally, it is mainly men who play it. Some players use a special method of breathing, called circular breathing. Air is breathed in through the nose at the same time as out through the mouth. This means that they can play a very long note without taking a breath.

Some say that the didgeridoo is the oldest instrument in the world.

Alphorn

The alphorn is a simple wooden horn. Its sound can be heard for many kilometres. Before telephones were invented, mountain dwellers in the Alps blew them to warn distant neighbours of avalanches (landslides of snow). Herdsmen used them to call in their cattle, too.

Snake charmers play a double clarinet. Snakes prefer not to attack, but most charmers keep just far enough away to be safe!

Snake charming

Indian snake charmers use the tiktiri, a type of clarinet. In fact, it is two clarinets in one. Two cane pipes are fitted into a **gourd**. The tiktiri's shrill sound is meant to put a snake in a trance so that it twists up from a basket. Snakes' ears are inside their head, so they do not hear the music the way that people can. It could be the music's vibrations that they sense. Some say that the snake is irritated by the charmer's waving instrument, so it stretches up in anger.

Air from elsewhere

Some aerophones are not blown but get their air from **bellows** or bags. Organs, bagpipes, and accordions are examples.

Dead sheep

The oldest bagpipes had a bag made from the whole skin of a dead sheep!

Bagpipes

Bagpipes are aerophones connected to a bag. The bag is filled with air from arm bellows or by mouth. The constant supply of air in the bag means that there is no need for a break in the music while the player takes a breath. A Scottish rock band called the Red Hot Chilli Pipers keeps the Scottish bagpipe tradition going.

Squeeze boxes

Accordions and concertinas are sometimes called squeeze boxes. This name comes from the way air is "squeezed" in and out of the bellows in these instruments.

Scottish bagpipes were sometimes called "warpipes". In Scotland and Ireland, bagpipes were sometimes played by armies marching into battle.

Comb composition

A **kazoo** is a wind instrument that uses air to make a buzzing sound. Make a kazoo and compose your own tune. If possible, ask a friend to join you so that you can write a two-part work.

You will need: tissue paper, plastic comb, paper, and pencil

Steps to follow:

1. Cut the paper into a rectangle to fold over your comb. Check the fold is along the points of the comb's teeth.

2. Hold one side of the paper-covered comb to your lips. Keeping your lips slightly apart, hum or sing notes. Experiment until you feel the paper **vibrate** and hear the kazoo make interesting sounds.

3. How loud or soft, fast or slow, can you play?

4. Imagine the flight of a bee: slowly searching for a flower, excitedly finding one, happily flying back to its nest. Match its flight and moods with different sounds, speeds, and tones on your kazoo.

5. Record your composition with a series of bee drawings. Use a key:

- Big/small bee drawing: play loud/soft
- Big wings/little wings: play fast/slow
- Position bee high or low: play high or low notes

As if by magic

Some instruments can play music all on their own. They do not need a musician because they work automatically. An example is a musical jewellery box. Inside the box, a **mechanism** plays the tunes.

Many mechanical instruments sound like a single instrument, while others sound like a whole orchestra!

Bells and chimes

In the Middle Ages (from around the 400s to the 1500s), mechanisms were made to play bells, chimes, and **hemispheres** in European clock towers. The mechanisms use rotating drums, ropes, cogwheels, levers, and hammers.

The 150-year-old clock in the tower of the Houses of Parliament sounds a large bell (called Big Ben) and four smaller bells. In 1976, the chiming mechanism smashed because one of the metal pieces had worn out. It took 9 months to mend.

A clockwork mechanism makes these figures (called Jack o' the clocks) hit a bell on this clock tower.

Look, no hands!

The self-player piano (called a pianola) does not need a musician. A paper roll with **perforations** (holes) is put inside the piano. As the roll rotates, it controls when the **mallets** strike the **keys**. Each roll produces a different tune.

Performances by some great players were recorded on rolls. Anyone could insert one of the rolls and pretend to be a famous concert pianist.

Music power

What powers or drives a mechanical instrument? For some clockwork and piano mechanisms you have to turn a handle (wind it up). Others run on electricity. Some chiming clocks are run by water pressure!

You do not need lessons to play an automatic piano.

Pipes and bellows

In the 1800s, the sound of barrel organs often filled the streets of **Western** cities. The players, called organ grinders, hoped that passers-by would pay for a tune. They often had a pet monkey to collect money and perform tricks.

The organ grinder turned a handle. This rotated a barrel with carefully positioned pins. The pins raised levers, which let air into one or more organ pipes to make the sounds. Turning the handle also worked **bellows**. These squeezed air into the organ pipes.

"A horrible noise"

Charles Babbage (1791–1871), an English mathematician and inventor, hated the sound of barrel organs on the streets of London. He wrote: "It is difficult to estimate the misery inflicted upon thousands of persons . . . by organ-grinders and other similar nuisances."

This street organ uses cards with perforations to produce the music.

Orchestra in a box

The orchestrion is a barrel organ made to sound like a band or orchestra. Like barrel organs, the music was on barrels. But as the barrel revolved, it played lots of musical instruments inside the machine.

A huge orchestrion called the Panharmonicon was built by an inventor named Johann Mälzel in 1804. It played a whole orchestra of instruments and could even set off muskets (guns) for dramatic effect. Mälzel also invented the **metronome** and one of the first dolls that could automatically speak and close its eyes!

Hurdy-gurdy

The hurdy-gurdy is a mechanical violin. A cranked wheel plays the strings. In the 1600s, poor travelling musicians in Eastern Europe tried to make a living playing them.

Some orchestrions have glass cases so you can see how they work.

Forces of nature

Some instruments are played by natural forces such as the wind and the sea. Wind chimes that hang outside are an example. The wind knocks shells or bells together to make the sound.

Aeolian harp

The Aeolian harp is an ancient instrument. It is like a harp but the wind makes the strings **vibrate**. It was named after Aeolus, the ancient Greek god of wind.

In China, strings are tied across some Chinese kites. In a breeze, the strings play sounds like an Aeolian harp.

Sea organ

The sea organ in Croatia has 35 large pipes tuned to different notes hidden under waterside steps. Waves of different sizes and speeds push air through the pipes to make different notes, and together the pipes play a chord.

The sea organ is on the coast of Croatia.

Making a wind chime

Make your own wind chime. You can hang it in a garden or just outside your window. Think about what you can hang on your chime. Remember to use items that:

- make a noise when the wind knocks them together
- are made of materials that won't be damaged by sunshine, wind, or rain
- look good.

Ideas: beads, seashells, steel washers, buttons, bells, and lengths of bamboo would work.

Steps to follow:

1. Gather together:
   - a stick about 15 centimetres (6 inches) long – it could be driftwood
   - items to hang (see above)
   - four or five 25-centimetre (10-inch) lengths of string, cotton, or nylon thread.

2. Thread your chosen items onto the strings. You may need to tie them so that they do not slip down.

3. Tie the ends of each thread to the stick so that they hang side by side. They must be close enough for the items to click together in the wind.

4. Hang your wind chime in a breezy place.

New ideas

Inventions and new technology will always lead to new instruments. New electronic instruments may even produce new sounds never heard before. Instrument makers will always want to break records. So far, the biggest and lowest-pitched saxophone is the contrabass. It is also the biggest woodwind instrument. However, something bigger may be invented in the future.

Art and music

When art and music blend, amazing new ideas appear. Australian artist Garry Greenwood made a 6-metre (20-foot) long leather instrument called the Windform. It looks beautiful and can be played.

Stand out from the crowd

Lots of people are interested in learning to play unusual instruments. It is fun to play something different from everyone else. Lots of folk instruments, such as the washtub, spoons, banjo, and djembe drums, are fun to play. Alternatively, you can invent and make your own instrument, and then decide how to play it!

Recycled music

People are worried about using up too many of the world's resources. Reusing materials is one answer. Many instruments are made of scrap. The Lost and Found Orchestra uses instruments made from rubbish, such as old vacuum cleaners, hose pipes, traffic cones, and shopping trolleys! Their music is powerful, rhythmic, and loud, and their performances can include 32 musicians and a large choir.

The Lost and Found Orchestra puts on an entertaining performance playing instruments made of reused objects – including the "plumpet", made from plumbers' pipe attached to traffic cones.

Glossary

aerophone instrument in which vibrating air makes the sound. Brass instruments (such as trumpets) are aerophones.

bellows bag on a musical instrument that blows out air. The bellows in an organ blows air into pipes.

bowed played with a bow. A violin is bowed to make the strings vibrate.

chordophone instrument in which the sound is made by vibrating stretched string(s). Pianos are chordophones.

civilization particular society or culture at a particular time

electrophone instrument in which the sound is made with electronics. Synthesizers are electrophones.

friction the rubbing of one surface against another surface

gourd hard skin of a hollowed-out fruit. A gourd acts as a resonator in many instruments, making the sound louder.

hemisphere bell-like instrument that is shaped like half a sphere

idiophone percussion instrument. The actual material that idiophones are made from makes their sound, such as two pieces of wood being clacked together.

kazoo instrument made using a comb and tissue paper

key lever that is pressed on a musical instrument

mallet small hammer. Mallets hit the strings inside a piano to sound the notes.

mechanism moving part. Mechanisms in some clocks make the hands move.

membrane thin sheet, such as an animal skin (leather) or paper. You strike a membrane to play a drum.

membranophone instrument in which the sound is made by a vibrating stretched skin, or membrane

metronome instrument that keeps a regular beat, used for music practice

neck part of a string instrument that sticks out

percussion family of instruments that are hit, shaken, scraped, or rubbed to make a sound

perforation hole

resonator (also called a soundbox) hollow cavity in an instrument, in which air vibrates to produce the sound

synthesizer electronic instrument that usually has a keyboard, like a piano

vibrate move backwards and forwards or up and down. The vibration of strings makes the sound in a guitar.

Western to do with the part of the world that includes Europe, the United States, and Australia

Find out more

Books
Musical Instruments of the World series (Franklin Watts, 2005)
World of Music series (Heinemann Library, 2008)

Websites
www.oddmusic.com
Listen to and look at all kinds of odd instruments on this site.

www.davidholt.com/music
Musician David Holt's musical instruments, plus more details
on how to play the spoons.

Places to visit
The Musical Museum
399 High Street
Brentford
Middlesex TW8 0DU
Tel. 020 8560 8108
www.musicalmuseum.co.uk
See a collection of mechanical instruments here.

Bate Collection
Faculty of Music
St Aldate's
Oxford OX1 1DB
Tel. 01865 276139
www.bate.ox.ac.uk
See over 1000 instruments from the Western orchestral music traditions.

Index